For Sadie,
May you enjoy the

Anna's in the Snow

a Sedona love story

**Story and images by
Beth Kingsley Hawkins**

Beth Kingsley Hawkins

ISBN: 978-0-615-81736-1

Printed in the USA

Dedication

I dedicate this book to my own grandchildren,
Maddie, Grace, Matthew and Garrett (all Kingsleys)
and to hummingbird lovers everywhere.

Acknowledgements

My appreciation goes to:

— My mother, an avid birder who studied the birds of
   the world at the zoo and then convinced my father to
   take her to see them in their natural habitat
   so she could add them to her life list.

— My father, who, being fond of travel (and my mother),
   always agreed to her quest.

— My husband, Ross, for his know-how and computer skills
   and for his commitment to maximizing the potential of my
   images.

— Kerri Esten for her talented graphic design skills.

— Jill McCutcheon, our next door neighbor,
   who shared 'her' nest with me on many levels.

— Kathy Dunham and Jackie Klieger for their feeling response
   to the story and images the first time I shared them.

— Mayte Garcia for loving the story so much
   and insisting that I commit to publishing it.

This is a very special love story.

Once upon a time, in a place not unlike this place,
and in a time not unlike this time,
there was a lovely Anna's hummingbird.

Her species of hummingbird was named long ago in honor of a French duchess
– Anna, the Duchess of Rivoli.

It was March – in the *very* early spring – and she had strong nesting instincts.
But, first she needed to find a man...... the *right* man......

One day she heard a beautiful sound that was music to her ears — a male
Anna's hummingbird had landed on a branch nearby and was singing away.

He wanted to make a good impression and had donned his most beautiful spring colors. To get her attention, he rose up 100 feet in the air until he was just a tiny speck in the sky. Then pointing his bill straight down like a hawk, he dove down – down – down – and just before he might have landed, he spread his tail feathers open in a fan.
As his two outer tail feathers began to vibrate they made one
loud snapping – clapping – whistling sound – just for her. But wait!
He wasn't finished yet; next he did a little shuttle dance back and forth
in front of her to make sure she was watching,
and then up, up, and up he rose again, seemingly all the way to the heavens.

She was dazzled by his brilliance.

He was irresistible! They were of one mind.

Soon she began to build a nest.
She very carefully chose a site on the branch of a cottonwood tree.

To a person looking at the nest, it seemed very exposed.
A few old, brown leaves were still clinging to the branch from the previous fall,
but otherwise it was just a bare branch amidst other bare branches.

She made the nest out of plant down and other natural materials
and anchored it to the tree with spider webbing.
HummerMom did all this by herself, with no help from the captivating
male. In fact, she didn't want "Mr. Neon" around to attract attention
and possibly invite predators.

She carefully danced around the nest, gluing it together with more spider
webbing. This would allow the nest to stretch a little as her babies grew bigger.
To cushion the babies and insulate them from the cold, she lined the nest
with unprocessed cotton that some thoughtful people had put out for her.

For finishing touches she attached tiny green lichen to the outside
for the practical purposes of camouflage and perhaps to satisfy
some ancient aesthetic need for beauty. She was a beauty in her own
right. As she turned her head, in the right light one could see just a few
magenta red feathers on her throat, reminiscent of the male's colorful gorget.

Satisfied with her nest creation, she laid her first perfect tiny white egg in it
– the size of a small Jelly Belly®.
And two days later, there were two perfect eggs in her nest.

This was no small task as she is the smallest bird in the world
and her eggs are the biggest of any bird in relation to the size of her
body. By comparison, in the same proportions as a hummingbird,
a human baby would weigh 22 pounds.
She sat patiently on the eggs for two weeks.

But on Sunday, the 18th of March it began to snow.

Her first baby hatched that day. She perched on the side of the nest and fed it
and then turned her other egg with her body.
It continued to snow non-stop.

On Monday the 19th, there was an accumulation of about 7 inches.

Her second baby hatched that day, and now she was perching briefly on the side
of the nest, feeding two. How would they be able to survive that storm?

HummerMom had carefully positioned her nest under a larger branch
which kept the snow away. Her body heat of 104 degrees kept the babies warm,
and if a snowflake did land on her, it melted.
She hunkered down in the nest, sealing it closed with her feathers.

Where would she find food?
Luckily there was a full hummingbird feeder nearby and several
at the neighbor's house. Also the cottonwood tree where she nested had holes
in its trunk made by the sapsucker; and in cold weather, when bugs were scarce,
she could drink the sap from the tree.

She had carefully chosen the site for her nest from another perspective.
She was in Sedona – in the Village of Oak Creek at the base of Cathedral Rock
– right on the Feminine Vortex!
She had a womb with a view.

She and her chicks could hear the gentle flowing sound of Oak Creek
and the rat-a-tat-tat of the kingfisher.

She could even see the Great Blue Heron
as he flew by to land on a nearby tree.

HummerMom had somehow managed to build her nest over a tiny branch lying on the larger branch. When the tree leafed out, the end of this smaller branch worked its way up through the nest and produced green leaves at the tip that served to conceal and protect the little ones.

Their most vulnerable time is when they are in the nest and can't fly,
so it is very important that they remain inconspicuous to any passing jay
or larger bird or snake or large lizard who might find them a delicacy.
HummerMom continued feeding them a delicious mixture of nectar and bugs
that they seemed to love and needed for their growth.

She kept very busy feeding herself and her two little ones around every twenty minutes.
She was a very attentive and devoted hummingbird mother.

In between feedings, the chicks had lots of time to dream big.
Perhaps they were dreaming that they would one day be able to fly like their mother.

Soon all the leaves on the tree leafed out and it was finally spring.
One evening, as the sun was setting, the shadow of the two chicks' heads
could be seen through the leaf as well as their open beaks peeking out above,
ever ready to be fed.

These hungry chicks required a lot of care, and she kept on feeding and feeding…

and they kept on growing and growing…

and growing.....until it was almost time to fly.

The nest was getting crowded now – the older chick was practicing his flight, whirring his wings while still clinging to the nest in adolescent-like behavior.
And, sure enough, three and a half weeks after he hatched, he was strong enough to fly.

The first chick's flight took him to a branch nearby
– not far from the nest –
so Mom could still find him…

...and find him she did!

The other nestling flew the coop as well...

and now the nest was empty – Success!
She was proud of her two new chicks
and would soon build another nest and start the process all over again.

The miracle of life unfolds,
and reminds us to stand still like the hummingbird
and know that all life is in the nature of the miraculous!

The beginning (not the end)